£6.99

What's inside!

MAKE THIS!

THIS WAY FOR LOONEY TUNES LUNACY!

WE HAVE TO GO BACK!! STOP!! HIT THE BRAKES!!

SORRY SIR! WE CAN'T STOP THE SHIP EVERYTIME SOMEONE -- I MEAN, *SOMETHING* -- FALLS OVER-BOARD.

PROPERTY OF D. DUCK

EVERYTHING I BROUGHT WAS IN THAT TRUNK! MY MONEY!! MY WARDROBE! -:CHOKE:- NOW I'LL HAVE TO BORROW *CLOTHES* FROM BUGS!

OUTTA MY WAY BLUTO! I GOTTA GET TO THE "WAVE-WATCHERS" SUITE PRONTO!

AHEM!! THE PASSENGERS WING IS *OFF-LIMITS* TO THE CREW! AND FIX YOUR BLAZER -- IT'S INSIDE OUT!!

FLIP

HEY, NOT BAD...

WAIT A MINUTE! I *AM* A PASSENGER!!

OH, *ARE* YOU? THEN I SUPPOSE YOU HAVE A *TICKET*?

GULP!

I THINK THIS REQUIRES A DELICATE APPROACH...

I DEMAND TO SEE THE *CAPTAIN*! I WANT THIS MESS STRAIGHTENED OUT *IMMEDIATELY*!

WHAT AN *AMAZING* COINCIDENCE! I'M THE CAPTAIN --

...AND *I* WANT *THIS* MESS STRAIGHTENED OUT *IMMEDIATELY*!

BUGS!!!

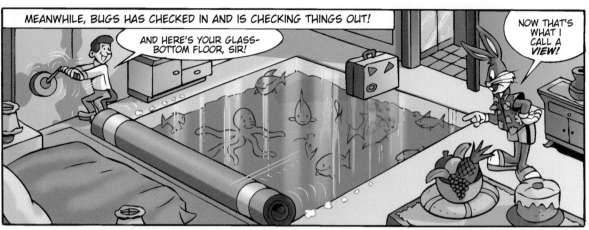

MEANWHILE, BUGS HAS CHECKED IN AND IS CHECKING THINGS OUT!

AND HERE'S YOUR GLASS-BOTTOM FLOOR, SIR!

NOW THAT'S WHAT I CALL A *VIEW!*

ENJOY YOUR CRUISE, SIR!

OH, I WILL, I WILL!

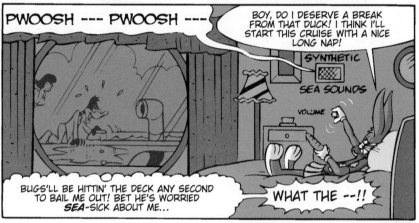

PWOOSH --- PWOOSH ---

BOY, DO I DESERVE A BREAK FROM THAT DUCK! I THINK I'LL START THIS CRUISE WITH A NICE LONG NAP!

SYNTHETIC

SEA SOUNDS

VOLUME

WHAT THE --!!

BUGS'LL BE HITTIN' THE DECK ANY SECOND TO BAIL ME OUT! BET HE'S WORRIED *SEA*-SICK ABOUT ME...

HEY! HEY!! WAKE UP, YOU DUMB --

NIGHTMARES I CAN HANDLE! IT'S THESE DUCK-FILLED *DAY-MARES* THAT GET TO ME!

WHOMP PWOOSH WHOMP

NOW, NOW! DON'T PESTER THE PASSENGERS!

HEH HE! WELL PUT PAL!

YANK

YOW!!

ATTENTION! DINNER IS NOW BEING SERVED IN THE DINING ROOM!

GREAT! THAT NAP MADE ME HUNGRY!

GREAT! AT LEAST THEY FEED YA ON THIS SLAVE-SHIP!

AHHH! THIS SMELLS GREAT!

GOURMET FOOD AND NO DAFFY IN SIGHT! THIS IS WHAT *I* CALL A VACATION!

CAVIAR?

DON'T MIND IF I DO!

WOW, WHAT *PORTIONS!* I SHOULDA ASKED FOR THE JUMBO -- *OW!*

THOSE ARE FOR THE *PASSENGERS!* NOW QUIT FOOLING AROUND AND SERVE!

HEY, YOU! FISH-EGG FELLA! OVER HERE!

COULD I HAVE A FEW HUNDRED OVER EASY?

GRR! THIS IS KILLIN' MY SUNNY-SIDE UP DISPOSITION!

THIS IS THE BEST CARROT-JUICE COCKTAIL I'VE EVER TASTED! THESE LITTLE UMBRELLAS REALLY ADD FLAVOUR!

THAT VOICE SOUNDS *VERY* FAMILIAR!

BUGS!! HELP ME!! TELL 'EM WHO I AM!

I'VE NEVER SEEN THIS DUCK BEFORE IN MY LIFE!

GROWL! *I* HAVE!!

YOU'RE BEING TRANSFERRED!

YOU ROTTEN RABBIT! I'LL GETCHA FOR THIS!!

TSK TSK! SUCH *RUDE* HELP!

"AND THE NIGHT IS STILL YOUNG ON THE *BIG BOBBER*. OH, THE ELEGANT LIFE ABOARD A SEALINER!"

Continued on page 16 ➡

Calamity Canyon!

It looks like Wile. E Coyote is about to take a dive! Add a splash of colour to this canyon calamity!

COLOUR GUIDE

1 2 3 4 5 6 7 8

PORKY PUZZLER

Oh dear! Taz has raided Porky's picnic basket. Find the words in the grid using the picture clues! There should be something left over for porky's lunch, can you work out what it is?

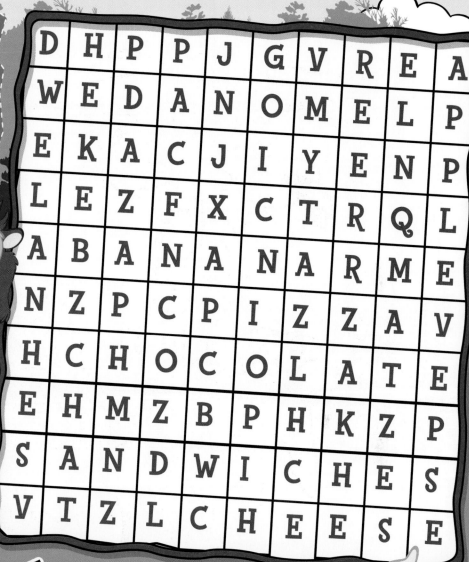

D	H	P	P	J	G	V	R	E	A
W	E	D	A	N	O	M	E	L	P
E	K	A	C	J	I	Y	E	N	P
L	E	Z	F	X	C	T	R	Q	L
A	B	A	N	A	N	A	R	M	E
N	Z	P	C	P	I	Z	Z	A	V
H	C	H	O	C	O	L	A	T	E
E	H	M	Z	B	P	H	K	Z	P
S	A	N	D	W	I	C	H	E	S
V	T	Z	L	C	H	E	E	S	E

ANSWERS ON PAGE 61!

Taz has left Porky with some _____

13

Taz Tissue Box!

YOU WILL NEED:

PVA glue, balloon, thick card, sticky tape, scissors, newspaper, paints and paintbrush, square box of tissues, pencil

1

Blow up the balloon, and cover it with 3-4 layers of torn up newspaper and PVA glue. Leave it to dry, and pop the balloon.

2

Cut the shape of the top of Taz's head from card, and tape it onto the balloon. Cut a hole in the knot end of the balloon and tape a circle of cardboard onto it. Make sure that the balloon will stand up on this circle. Cover with more papier maché.

3

Paint the balloon white, and draw or trace Taz's features onto it. Cut out the shape of Taz's mouth, and cut a square hole in the back of the balloon, large enough to take a square box of tissues.

4

Paint Taz with two shades of brown paint, and add details with black, white and red paint. When it's dry pop in your tissue box!

Continued from page 11

YES, THERE'S NOTHING LIKE A SEA CRUISE FOR REST AND RELAXATION! JUST ASK BUGS AND DAFFY...

SIX A.M.! TIME TO WAKE UP, MR. BUNNY. RISE AND SHINE!

ZZZZZ

SIX BELLS!!! ALL DUCKS ON DECK! THIS MEANS *YOU*!!!

WHUZZIT!!

YER PERSONALISED WAKE-UP CALL, MATEY! GET WITH IT! 'TIS THE 21ST CENTURY!

TING-A-LING

♪ BREAKFAST, SIR! ♪

ZZZZ-

IS THIS A DREAM *VACATION* OR WHAT?

THIS IS WHAT I CALL BEIN' AT THE BOTTOM OF THE CORPORATE *RIGGING*!

SOAP

SOAP

RUMBLE

YUM! BREAKFAST IN BED! WHAT A GREAT INVENTION!

CHOP

CHIP

CHOP

CHIP

SEA LOOPS

YES, SIR! YOU DON'T WANT TO DINE ON DECK *THIS* MORNING... IT MAY BE NICE WEATHER FOR *DUCKS*, BUT CERTAINLY NOT FOR OUR *GUESTS*!

I *HATE* THAT EXPRESSION! YOW!!!

ZAP

YEOW

CRACKLE

POP

SOAP

MMM...DEE-LISH! SAY, WHAT'S THE GUY IN THE *NEXT* SUITE HAVING?

SNAP

SMELLS LIKE SOMETHING FROM THE GRILL, SIR!

THIS *REALLY* BURNS ME UP!!!

THAT SPLENDID AFTERNOON...

SIGN UP *NOW!*

PASSENGER'S PLAYTIME

EXTRA-CREW-ICULAR ACTIVITIES

SHUFFLE-BOARD LESSONS	PUSH TUSH DANCING	CHECKERS	MOP	FORE & AFT SWEEPERS	PUCK-DUCK
Bugs Bunny	*Della*				
Katie & Dana	*DAVE*				

I'LL SHUFFLE THAT BUNNY'S BOARDS... BUT FIRST I GOTTA FIGURE A WAY TO GET NEAR HIM...

"PUCK DUCK"? SOUNDS *PERFECT!*

NOW PUT YOUR OTHER HAND HERE AND...

I'M GONNA LOVE THIS GAME!

POOSH

HOORAY! A GOAL-IN-ONE!

SHOOOSH

BONK-

FLIP

ZOOM

BONKA

OOOPS! GUESS I OWE YA A PUCK...

HAVE 'EM PUT IT ON YER *HOSPITAL* BILL!

THIS HAPPENS ALL THE TIME! THAT'S WHY WE HAVE A --

SPLASH

GURGLE

?

"PUCK DUCK"!! LETS GO!!! PUCK OVERBOARD!!

Y!!

BETWEEN YOU AND ME, I *STILL* THINK I SCORED!

"BY DINNERTIME..."

GEE, I WAS *GREAT!* I THINK I "SHUFFLED A *THOUSAND*"!

TERRIBLE PUCK-DUCK, THOUGH! HE DIDN'T TAKE TO THE WATER *AT ALL!*

GRRR-URRGLE!

FOUR A.M..

ATTENTION! ALL DUCKS ON DECK! THIS MEANS *YOU!!!*

GROAN! I CAN'T TAKE ANOTHER DAY OF THIS!

...ESPECIALLY IF IT'S GONNA RAIN LIKE *YESTERDAY!*

I'M THROUGH BUSTIN' MY BEAK FOR THIS CRUMMY CRUISE-OUTFIT! I'LL JUST SQUIRT THESE SUDS AND LET THE NEXT *TIDAL WAVE* DO THE WASH WHILE I TAKE A SNOOZE!

BUFF

SQUIRRT

DECK VARNISH

BEAUTIFUL MORNING, EH, ENSIGN? CALMEST SEA I'VE EVER SEEN!

ZZZ ZZZ

DAZZLING! ..AND NOT A *DROP* OF RAIN!

WOW! ALMOST 8:00! BETTER RING THE BREAKFAST BELL!

YESSIR!

CLANG

WHLIZZIT!

NOW, THAT'S WHAT I CALL *SHINE!* FROM NOW ON, MOTHER NATURE CAN DO *ALL* MY CHORES...

THIS'LL MAKE A PERFECT SOUVENIR -- ALL I GOTTA DO IS ADD A *RABBIT*!

HEAVY DUTY GIFT SHOPPE

PIRATE IN A BOX ▶

PEG-LEG-KIT (U-CARVE-IT!)

UH OH! I LEFT MY WALLET IN MY LOCKER! *DAVY JONES'S* LOCKER, THAT IT...

THAT'S OKAY, MATEY! IF YER ON THE CREW, YE KIN JUST *SIGN* FER IT!

GREAT!

POINT ME TO THE GANGPLANK! I NEVER WANT TO SEE SEA AGAIN!

IS EVERYTHING SATISFACTORY, SIR?

YOU BET!

SALE

KEEP THE CHANGE! JUST BE SURE THE CAPTAIN GETS THIS LOG-BOOK BEFORE THAT DUCK HITS THE DOCK!

YES, SIR!

$12.99

OLD SALT OUTFIT

LET ME GO, YOU BRINEY BUM! I *DEMAND* DRY LAND!

SORRY, DUCKIE! ACCORDING TO THIS, YOU JUST SIGNED ON FOR TWO MORE WEEKS OF DECK DUTY!

TWO MORE DAFFY-FREE WEEKS! WHO SAYS I DON'T KNOW HOW TO *DRESS FOR SUCCESS!*?

the End

Water-Fools!

Who gave Taz the paddle? It looks like our toons are about to take a plunge! Before they go over the edge, can you spot six differences between the two pictures?

ANSWERS ON PAGE 61!

23

MEMORY MADNESS

Study the picture below for a minute then cover it with a piece a paper and answer the questions on the right!

It's question time!

1 What book is Porky reading? ☐

a) **History: Can You Dig It?**
b) **THIS OLD TOMB**
c) **SECRETS OF THE PYRAMIDS**

2 What animal is Yosemite Sam riding?

a) A camel
b) A horse
c) A llama ☐

3 What colour book is Road Runner carrying? ☐

a)   b)   c)

4 Who is climbing on the Sphynx?

a) Daffy
b) Bugs ☐
c) Marvin

5 Who is flying?

a) Yosemite Sam
b) Road Runner ☐
c) Wile E

6 What is Bugs holding in his right hand? ☐

a)   b)   c)

7 In what country does this scene take place?

a) Egypt
b) France ☐
c) America

8 What are the little Egyptian ants building?

a) A house
b) A pyramid ☐
c) A wall

ANSWERS ON PAGE 61!

How did you do?

Are you a brainiac or did you have a memory meltown? Check out your scores here!

0-3 Memory Meltdown!

4-6 Mediocre Memory!

7-8 Master of Memory!

SHIVER ME TIMBERS *

WB100

Story: Dave King Art: George Wildman Letterer: Bob Pinaha Colorist: Duendes del Sur

E-BUH-BUH B-OHH, BOY. I FEEL *TERRIBLE!* I ALWAYS GET *S-SEA* SICK!

THE GEORGE BAILEY

GEE! THEN I GUESS YOU SHOULDN'T BE THE CAPTAIN OF A *SHIP*, UH, CAPTAIN?

SO HERE WE ARE, CAST ADRIFT BY AN OFFICIOUS CAPTAIN AND NOT A CARROT IN SIGHT!

AT LEAST WE CAN WORK ON OUR TANS!

SAY, *WHAT'S THAT?!*

IT'S A *MESSAGE IN A BOTTLE!*

HELP!

MAYBE IT'S A COUPLE OF TICKETS TO *PISMO BEACH!*

FEH!

HELP!

IS IT A *TREASURE MAP?*

NAAH! IT'S A NOTE FROM THE CAPTAIN OF THE *GEORGE BAILEY,* OUT OF NEW ENGLAND!

HE SAYS THEY NEED HELP. THAT THEY'VE BEEN ATTACKED BY THE BLOODTHIRSTY MARAUDING CREW OF PIRATE *YOSEMITE SAM!*

NOTHING COULD HELP THEM NOW! I'VE HEARD TALES ABOUT THAT GUY. HE'S ONE SICK SAILOR I HOPE *NEVER* TO MEET!

I WON'T TELL YOU ABOUT THE GOLD, THEN!

GOLD, YOU SAY? WELL, WE REALLY *SHOULD* HELP OUT A FELLOW *MATE,* DON'T YOU THINK?

AND MOMENTS LATER...

I'M SURE YOU'RE DOING THIS FOR ALL THE RIGHT REASONS, DAFFY...

...BUT, LIKE, EHHH... YOU DIDN'T SEEM TO THINK RESCUING THESE GUYS WAS SUCH A GREAT IDEA!

UNTIL I MENTIONED THE GOLD!

WHOOOOOOOSHH

I HOPE YOU'RE NOT BESMIRCHING MY GOOD CHARACTER!

HEAVEN FORBID!

SO WHAT MAKES YOU THINK WE'RE HEADING IN THE RIGHT DIRECTION?

HORRIBLE, BLOODTHIRSTY PIRATES THIS WAY!

OH, JUST A HUNCH!

I'D TURN BACK IF I WERE YOU!

DURN IT, WHUT'S TH' MATTER WITH YA ALL?

I WUZ JEST GETTIN' TA TH' BEST PART!

I HOPE HE MEANS THE END!

I CAN'T STAND NO MORE! *SCURVY* WAS EASIER TO GET RID OF THAT THIS GUY! ⇥SOB!⇤

WHY, ANYONE'D GIT TH' IDEA THET YOU WUZ ALL BORED WITH TH' TALES OF MAH ADVENTURES!

P-PERISH THE THOUGHT.

WELL, YA HAD ALL JEST BETTER GIT USED TA IT!

AH BROUGHT YA ALL BACK HERE FER A REASON!

THE LONG WINTER IS-A-DRAWIN' IN AND AH NEED SOME COMPANY!

YOU BOYS IS GONNA BE HERE, LISTENING TO MAH STORIES...

...FER TH' NEXT *FIVE MONTHS!*

AAAARGH GAAARGHH

EEYAAHHH

Continued on page 38 ➡

34

Name that toon!

Crack the crossword using the picture clues, then unjumble the letters in the shaded squares to reveal the mystery toon.

Across

1. 
4. 
6.

ANSWERS ON PAGE 61!

Down

2. 
3. 
5.

The mystery toon is:

_ _ _ _ _ _

_ _ _ _ _ _

Code Breaker

Are you a super sleuth? Use the decoder below to help Granny work out what Tweety is trying to say.

ANSWERS ON PAGE 6

36

MARTIAN MASTERPIECE

Use the grids below to draw Marvin and K-9. When you've finished add some colour to your cosmic creations!

Continued from page 34

EVENTUALLY...

SHEEESH! WHO WAS THE ARCHITECT FOR THIS PLACE? *COUNT DRACULA?!*

THAT MUST BE THE CASTLE'S GREAT HALL!

GULP!

THERE'S AN OPEN WINDOW! LET'S SEE IF WE CAN CLIMB UP!

MORE HARD WORK! I HOPE THE GOLD'S WORTH...I MEAN, I HOPE THOSE SAILORS ARE OKAY! HEH!

BOY...THAT'S A LONG DROP!

AHHH...IT'S NOT SO BAD!

SPLOOSH

UNTIL YOU HIT THE *BOTTOM*, THAT IS!

AND SO...

GEE, YOU'VE DONE B-BUH-BUH-BRILLIANTLY! NOW THE GOLD CAN MAKE ITS WAY SAFELY TO ENGLAND!

IT WAS NOTHING, DOC!

SO CLOSE! I WAS *SO* CLOSE ➤SIGH!◄

BUT WHERE'S PIRATE SAM?

OH, I THINK HE WENT TO *FEED THE FISH!* HEH! HEH! HEH!

NOT ME! NOT ME, YA EEDJIT SHARK! **HEEELP!**

THAT'S ALL FOLKS!

Barmy Bugs

Can you join the dots to find out which water sport Bugs has taken up?

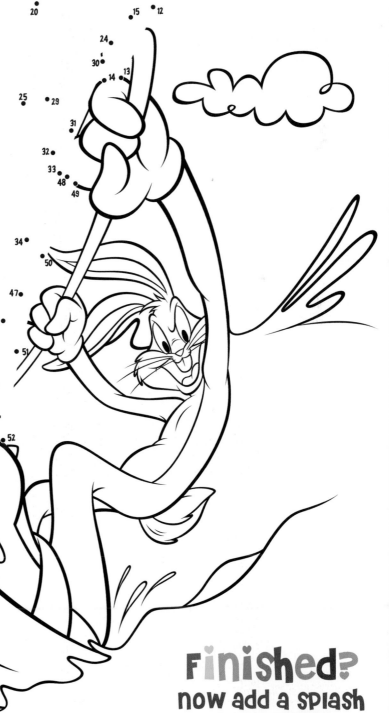

FiNiShED?
now add a splash of colour!

Skate Park Puzzler!

AWESOME! Daffy and his pals are pulling some tricks and flips at the skate park. See if you can crack this picture puzzler!

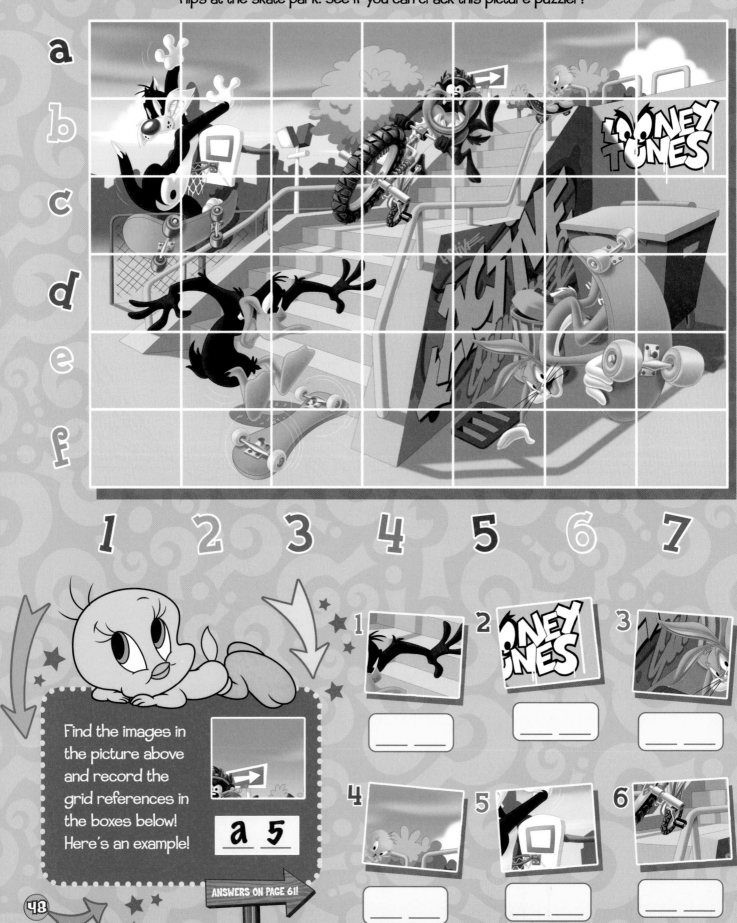

Find the images in the picture above and record the grid references in the boxes below! Here's an example!

a 5

ANSWERS ON PAGE 61!

1

2

3

4

5

6

• PAPARAZZI RABBIT •

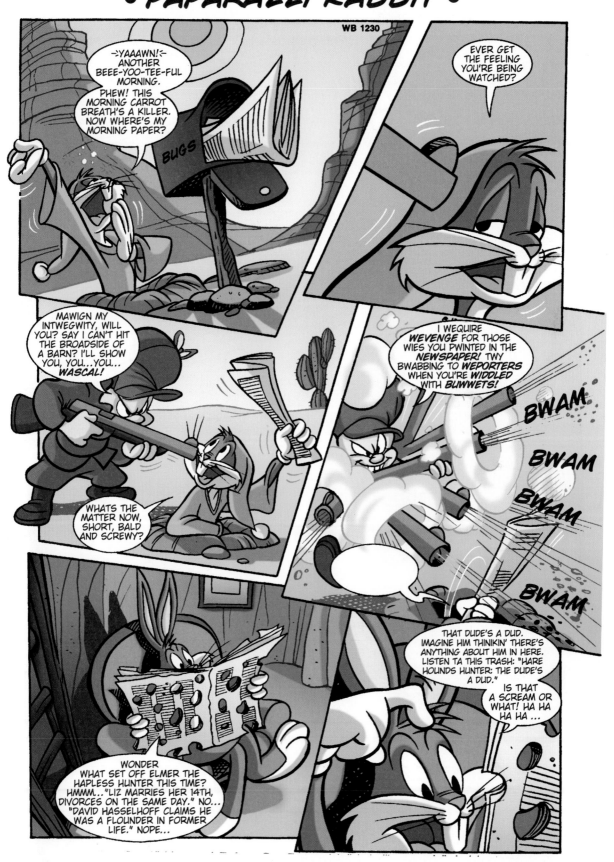

Continued on page 56

53

Totem Pole!

Get creative and make your own totem pole game! Follow the simple steps to create this great bedroom boredom buster!

wobble!

creeaaakk!

YOU WILL NEED:

five crisp tubes
PVA glue
newspaper
black felt tip pen
thick card
scissors
paints and paintbrush

1 Paint each of the crisp tubes with a bright colour and leave to dry.

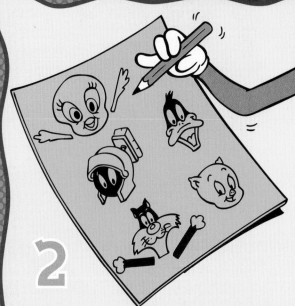

2 Draw or trace Looney heads onto card and cut them out. Draw Tweety's wings and Sylvester's arms too.

3 Paint the Looney heads and arms and outline each one with black pen.

4 Glue the heads onto the tubes. Ask an adult to help you cut slots in Tweety and Sylvester's tubes, and push the arms through.

 When the totem pole is dry, you can use it in games of throwing or bowling. Stack up the pots and take turns knocking them down!

Continued from page 53

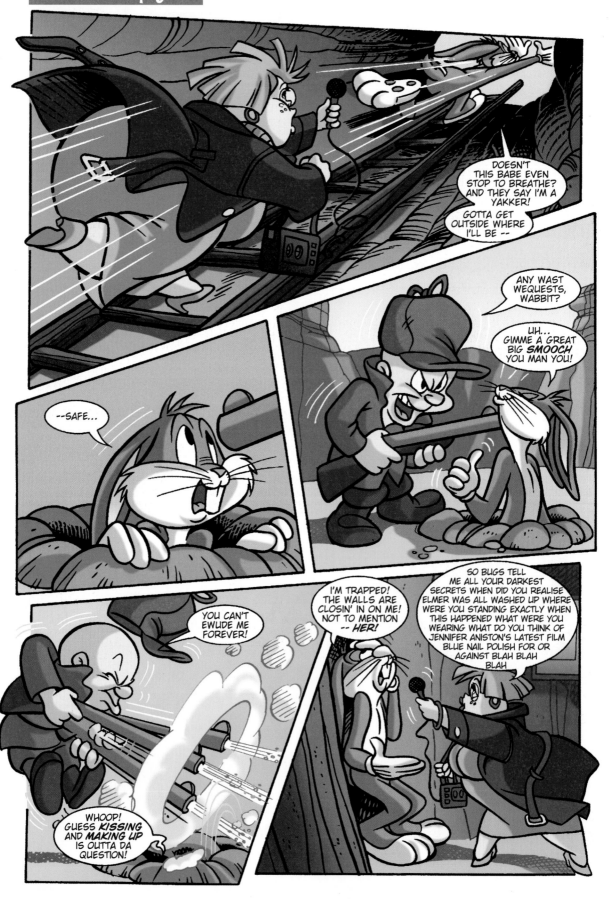

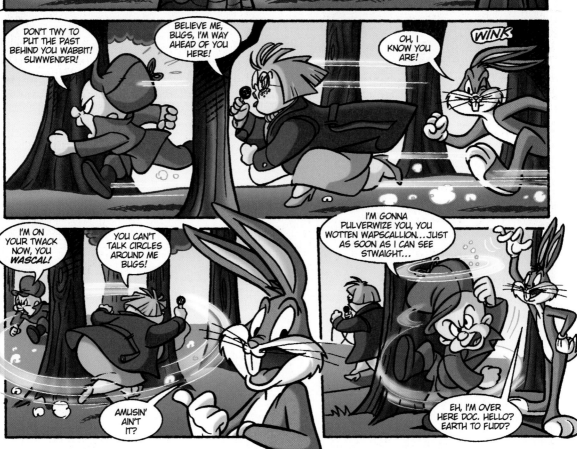

WAH-HA-HAH. *I GIVE UP!* THAT NEWSPAPER WAS *WIGHT!* I'LL NEVER TWAP THAT *WABBIT!*

AWRIGHT. I CAN'T TAKE NO MORE. I HATE TA SEE A *GROWN MAN CRY.*

BUCK UP, BUCKO. I'LL HELP YA.

YOU WILL?

WOULD I LIE TO YOU?

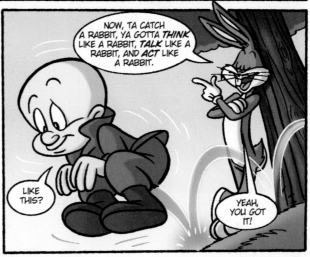

NOW, TA CATCH A RABBIT, YA GOTTA *THINK* LIKE A RABBIT, *TALK* LIKE A RABBIT, AND *ACT* LIKE A RABBIT.

LIKE THIS?

YEAH, YOU GOT IT!

BUT WE AIN'T FINISHED YET. NOW, TO CATCH *ME*, YA GOTTA *THINK* LIKE ME, YA GOTTA *TALK* LIKE ME, AND *ACT* LIKE ME.

UH...I'LL TWY. IT'S TEWWIBLY DIFFICULT.

AIN'T IT DA *THRUTH?* THAT'S WHAT MAKES ME *SO SPECIAL.*

EH, WHAT'S UP, DOC? HEH - HEH - HEH.

MASTERFUL, DOC. THAT'S THE ONLY WORD I CAN THINK OF.

THE ONLY *POLITE* WORD, THAT IS.

ANSWERS!

Page 23 - Water Fools

Page 13 - Porky Puzzler

D	H	P	P	J	G	V	R	E	A
W	E	D	A	N	O	M	E	L	P
E	K	A	C	J	I	Y	E	N	P
L	E	Z	F	X	C	T	R	Q	L
A	B	A	N	A	N	A	R	M	E
N	Z	P	C	P	I	Z	Z	A	V
H	C	H	O	C	O	L	A	T	E
E	H	M	Z	B	P	H	K	Z	P
S	A	N	D	W	I	C	H	E	S
V	T	Z	L	C	H	E	E	S	E

Taz has left Porky with some SAUSAGES

Page 22 - Wabbit Hunt!

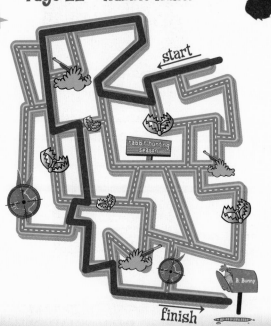

start

rabbit hunting season

finish

B. Bunny

Page 24-25 - Memory Madness

1. b   5. c
2. a   6. b
3. b   7. a
4. a   8. b

Page 35 - Name That Toon!

ACROSS: DOWN:
1. Tweety Pie   2. Elmer Fudd
4. Sylvester   3. Bugs Bunny
6. Daffy Duck   5. Porky Pig

The mystery toon is Road Runner!

Page 36 - Code Breaker

Tweety is saying : "I tawt I taw a puddy tat!"

Page 48 - Skate Park Puzzler

1. d 3   4. a 6
2. b 7   5. b 2
3. e 5   6. c 4